COLOURS AROUND ME

Green

Anita Loughrey

QED Publishing

What is green?

Green is a colour.

This is the colour green.

Look at the picture of the classroom.

What can you see that is green?

Who is going to the green tent?

Follow the paths to find out.

Matt

Fay

Olga

Poppy

3

Finding green

Point to the things that are green.

How many green things can you see?

Answer: 4 green things

Matching green

Look at the fish.

Point to the two green fish.

Hungry caterpillar

Help the caterpillar through the maze to get to the juicy green lettuce.

How many green fruits and vegetables does the caterpillar pass on the way?

Answer: 5 green fruits and vegetables

Green shapes

Green things can be different shapes.

How many green squares can you see?

How many green circles can you see?

Answer: 3 green squares, 2 green circles

How many green rectangles can you see?

How many green triangles can you see?

What green shapes can you see around you?

9

Big and small

Green things can be different sizes.

bigger

big

small

biggest

smaller

smallest

Odd ones out

Some things here
are the wrong colour.

pumpkin

pig

monkey

corn cob

grasshopper

12

rose

tree

sunflower

rabbit

leaf

which things
should be green?

Answer: The grasshopper, the leaf and the tree should be green.

Shades of green

Green can be different shades.

dark green

dark green

dark green and green

green

light green

light green

What shades of green
can you see around you?

Green at the river

Point to all the green things you can see at the river.

frog

dragonfly

fish

boat

reeds

lily pad

newt

What other green things might you see at a river?

17

Green in the home

Point to all the green things you can see in the kitchen.

stool

clock

tablecloth

knife   fork   spoon

jug

apron

bowl

Have you ever seen
any of these green
things in a kitchen?

19

Green is for growing

Lots of things are growing in this garden. What green things can you see?

water butt

compost bin

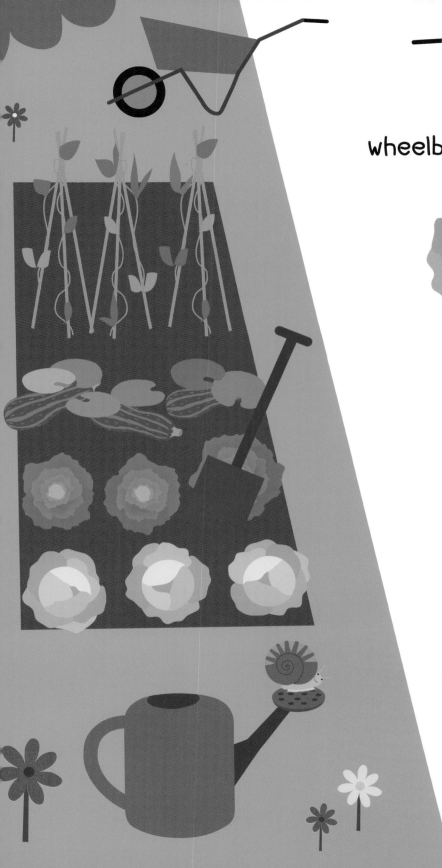

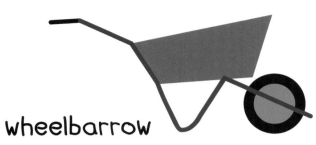
wheelbarrow

lettuce

gardening fork

flowerpot

Look outside. What green things can you see growing?

Green on the farm

Point to the green things you can see on the farm.

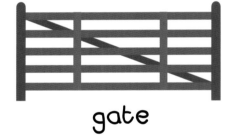

gate

boots

hat

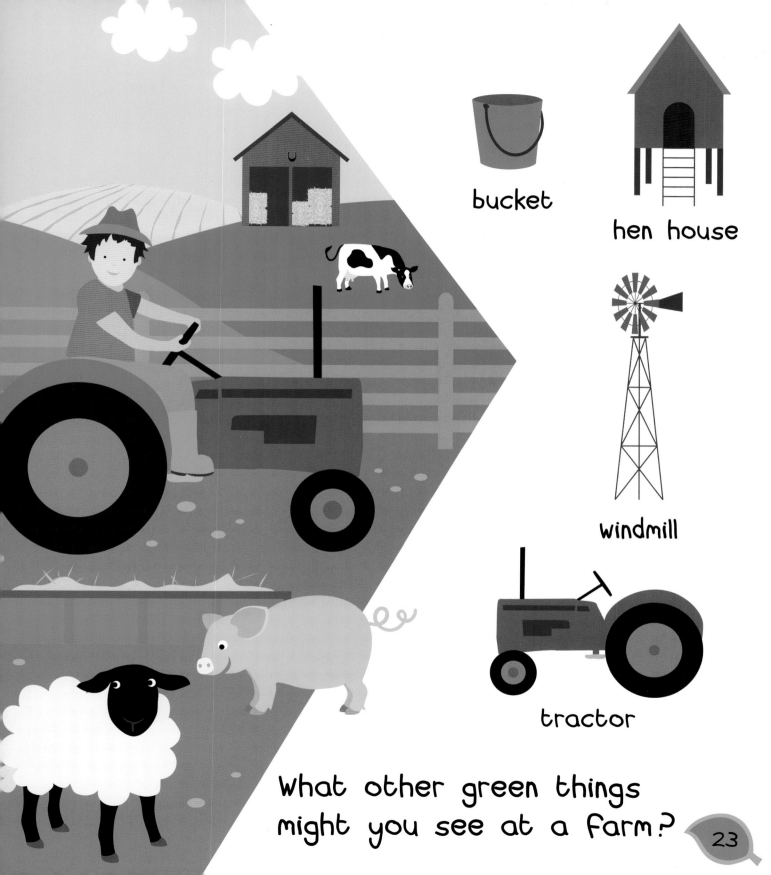

bucket

hen house

windmill

tractor

What other green things might you see at a farm?

23

Notes for parents and teachers

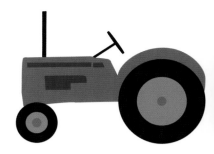

This book has been designed to help children to recognize the colour green and to distinguish green from other colours. The vibrant activities make learning fun and use the environment around them to reinforce what they have learned.

• Read the instructions to the child. Allow time for the child to think about the activity. Encourage them to discuss what they see.

• Praise the child if they recognize the items in the book. If any of the items are unfamiliar, explain what they are and where they might be found.

• If possible, take the child into the environment you have talked about so that they can observe items pictured in this book. Encourage the child to spot green objects using ideas from this book.

• Remember to keep it fun. Stop before the child gets tired or loses interest, then continue on another day. Children learn best when they are relaxed and enjoying themselves. It is best to help them experience new concepts in small steps.

Other activities you could try:

• Play games such as 'I spy': saying "I spy with my little eye a green thing beginning with…". If the child is not yet familiar with the alphabet, you could say the initial sound of the word rather than the letter name.

• Cut pictures from catalogues and magazines of different-coloured objects and ask the child to sort them, or match them to the pictures in this book.

• Ask the child what green things they can see when you are outside, at home, or looking in other books.

• Experiment with colour using different media such as paint, crayons, pastels and coloured paper.

Illustrator: Sue Hendra
Editor: Lauren Taylor
Designer: Fiona Hajée
Educational consultant: Jillian Harker

Copyright © QED Publishing 2011

First published in the UK in 2011 by
QED Publishing
A Quarto Group company
226 City Road
London EC1V 2TT

www.qed-publishing.co.uk

A catalogue record for this book is available from the British Library.

ISBN 978 1 84835 537 8

Printed in China

24